A My Name Is...

W9-BRX-001

Alice Lyne

illustrated by

Lynne Cravath

SCHOLASTIC INC.
New York Toronto London Auckland Sydney
Mexico City New Delhi Hong Kong

ISBN 0-439-27462-1

Copyright © 1997 by Alice Lyne.
Illustrations copyright © 1997 by Lynne Cravath.
All rights reserved.
Published by Scholastic Inc., 555 Broadway, New York, NY 10012,
by arrangement with Whispering Coyote Press.
SCHOLASTIC and associated logos are trademarks and/or registered
trademarks of Scholastic Inc.

12 11 10 9 8 7 6 5 4 3 2 1   1 2 3 4 5 6/0

Printed in the U.S.A.   09

First Scholastic printing, January 2001

Book design by Our House
Text was set in 16-point Kabel Bold

My name is Xavier,
My best friend's name is Xerxes,
We live in Xanadu,
And we sell xylophones.

My name is Violet,
My best friend's name is Vinny,
We live in West Virginia,
And we sell waffles.

Very
Wonderful
Waffles

My name is Ursula,
My best friend's name is Uli,
We live in Uruguay,
And we sell umbrellas.

My name is Teena,

My best friend's name is Tammy,

We live in Tallahassee,

And we sell turtles.

My name is Reba,
My best friend's name is Rita,
We live in Sicily,
And we sell salami.

Qq

My name is Quentin,
My best friend's name is Quincy,
We live in Quebec,
And we sell quail.

Pp

My name is Pedro,
My best friend's name is Pablo,
We live in Puerto Rico,
And we sell parrots.

N n
O o

My name is Nathan,
My best friend's name is Nola,
We live in Ohio,
And we sell oil.

M
m
My name is Maya,
My best friend's name is Mickey,
We live in Minneapolis,
And we sell martians.

My name is Lisa,
My best friend's name is Lilly,
We live in Louisiana,
And we sell lobsters.

My name is Jackson,
My best friend's name is Janice,
We live in Kyoto,
And we sell kittens.

I i

My name Ian,
My best friend's name is Ida,
We live in Indonesia,
And we sell iguanas.

H h

My name is Hannah,
My best friend's name is Harry,
We live in Honolulu,
And we sell hippos.

My name is Frankie,
My best friend's name is Freda,
We live in Guatemala,
And we sell giants.

Ee

My name is Ethel,
My best friend's name is Emma,
We live in Ethiopia,
And we sell elephants.

My name is David,
My best friend's name is Daniel,
We live in Damascus,
And we sell diamonds.

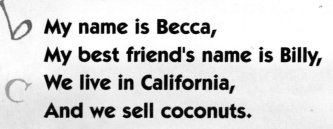

My name is Becca,
My best friend's name is Billy,
We live in California,
And we sell coconuts.

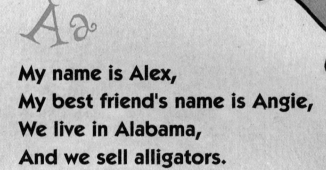

Aa

My name is Alex,
My best friend's name is Angie,
We live in Alabama,
And we sell alligators.

My name is Yuri,
My best friend's name is Yoda,
We live in Yugoslavia,
And we sell yo-yo's.

ZEE END!

My name is Zelma,
My best friend's name is Zoe,
We live in Zambia,
And we sell zippers.